A COMPANION TO THE BOOK

Lovestruck
Bible Study Guide

SHARON JAYNES

TABLE OF CONTENTS

•••

I'm so glad you've decided to dig deeper into the Song of Solomon. I've given you a lot of commentary in Lovestruck, and we've deciphered much of the secret code of the book. In the study guide, I'm going to do my best to hand you the shovel so that you can dig deeper into God's Word for yourself. This is your space—your time to make discoveries, find hidden treasure, and reflect on how this heart-stirring, romantic book relates to you, your marriage, and your man. Strap on your mining helmet and turn on the helmet light. Dig deep. Grow strong.

Love well, Sharon

•••

Introduction

What stood out to you most in the introduction of *Lovestruck*?

Would you say that your views on sex are formed more by culture or the Bible?

Please don't feel guilty if your answer is "culture." Many don't even realize that the Bible talks about sex in a positive way.

How has culture's views on sex affected those around you? Give a few examples.

How has the culture's views on sex affected you?

Before we begin the study of the Song of Solomon, what does 2 Timothy 3:16-17 tell us about the Word of God—the Bible? What are the four reasons for studying the Bible listed in this verse?

The Hebrew word, "theopneustos" is literally translated "God-breathed." Some translations say, "inspired by God" (NLT, NASB) or "given by inspiration of God" (KJV).

The Noah Webster Dictionary of 1828 says this about the word inspiration INSPIRATION, noun [Latin inspiro.]

> 1. The act of drawing air into the lungs; the inhaling of air; a branch of respiration, and opposed to expiration.

> 2. The act of breathing into any thing.

> 3. The infusion of ideas into the mind by the Holy Spirit; the conveying into the minds of men, ideas, notices or monitions by extraordinary or supernatural influence; or the communication of the divine will to the understanding by suggestions or impressions on the mind, which leave no room to doubt the reality of their supernatural origin.

> 4. The infusion of ideas or directions by the supposed deities of pagans.

> 5. The infusion or communication of ideas or poetic spirit, by a superior being or supposed presiding power; as the inspiration of Homer or other poet.

Circle the one that you feel most applies to the Bible.

While the English word "inspired" has many different shades of meaning, the Hebrew word "theopneustos" is quite clear. Explain the difference.

How did God bring the body of Adam to life? (Genesis 2:7)

How is this similar to what happens in us when we read the Bible?

Who did Jesus say that He is? (John 14:6)

Read John 1:1-3 and note how the words "word" and "life" relate to one another.

What conclusion can you draw from the reason God made sure The Song of Solomon is included in Scripture?

What are you most excited about in studying The Song of Solomon?

Write down three questions you have regarding The Song of Solomon before we begin.

Lesson One

The Mystery of Physical Attraction

. . . .

Even though we did not get all the way through Song of Solomon 1 in *Lovestruck* Chapter 1, take time to read it in its entirety.

One thing we will notice throughout the Song is that it is written mostly in the female's voice. Scan through the headings of the eight chapters in your Bible and note how many subheadings are the Shulammite's (female's) voice, and how many are Solomon's (male's) voice.

According to Chapter 1, what attracted the Shulammite to Solomon?

What attracted Solomon to the Shulammite?

How does the Shulammite describe Solomon's kisses in 1:2?

How are the effects of wine and a passionate kiss similar?

When was the first time you kissed your husband? Describe how it made you feel.

One of the first things that a man and woman notice about each other during the initial attraction phase is physical appearance. However, physical attraction is not enough to sustain a relationship. The Shulammite was attracted to Solomon's appearance, but also to his character.

Define character.

Give several synonyms.

What aspect of your husband's character drew you to him initially?

What do the following verses tell us about someone's character? How is it formed? Romans 5:3-5

What are signs of godly character? Galatians 5:22-23

Make a list of the qualities of godly character listed in Colossians 3:12-14.

What do you think it means to "put on" the qualities of character listed in Colossians 3:12-14?

How does Romans 13:14 echo Colossians 3:12-14?

What does Solomon tell us about the value of a good name in Proverbs 22:1?

The Shulammite described Solomon's name as "oil poured out," or "perfumed oil poured out." Read the following and note how "oil poured" is referenced. How was it used? What was its purpose?

Exodus 29:7

Exodus 30:23-25

1 Samuel 16:13

Mark 14:3

John 12:3

From these few verses, how would Solomon have interpreted the Shulammite's comparison of his name to "perfumed oil poured out"?

Read through Proverbs 31:10-31. What did Solomon's mother tell him to look for in the character of a good wife?

Which of those qualities of the Shulammite are mirrored in Song of Solomon 1?

Proverbs 31:10 says, "A wife of noble character who can find? She is worth far more than rubies." Read that verse in several Bible translations.

Biblehub.com and Biblegateway.com are helpful sources when comparing translations. What other words do you find to describe her character in 31:10?

The Hebrew word translated "noble," "excellent," "virtuous," and "capable" is the Hebrew word *chayil*. It can be translated "strength, wealth, mighty warrior, excellent, noble character, woman of valor, virtuous woman.

What aspect of your character do you think attracted your husband to you initially...after he got past the fact that you were the most beautiful woman he had ever seen?

What warning does Proverbs 6:25 give to men?

What does "in your heart" mean?

Being captured and captivated are very different. Look up the definitions and compare and contrast the two.

Would you say that Solomon is captured or captivated by the Shulammite?

What did the Shulammite call Solomon in 1:7a?

In the original Hebrew, "You whom I love" is literally, "you whom my soul loves." The soul includes the mind, will, and emotions.

How do you love your husband with your mind?

How do you love your husband with you will?

How do you love your husband with your emotions?

How do you let your husband know that you love him with your mind, will, and emotions?

Let me put that another way—how will you let your husband know that you love him with your mind, will, and emotions this week?

Reflect

What physical features initially attracted you to your husband?

What physical features do you think initially attracted your husband to you? (You might want to ask him this question.)

When you were dating your husband, did you ever practice writing his name? I know I did. Take a moment and simply write your husband's full name.

When you were dating your husband, did he wear a certain cologne? Can you still remember it today? How does it make you feel when he wears it? If he doesn't wear it any longer, consider purchasing him a bottle.

Is there a certain fragrance that your husband likes for you to wear? How do you think it makes him feel when you wear it? If you haven't worn it lately, you might want to dust it off.

What impacted you most in *Lovestruck* chapter 1?

What impacted you most in *Lovestruck* Bible Study Guide Lesson 1?

Lesson Two

The Deepening of Desire

In *Lovestruck* Chapter 1, we took a quick look at Genesis 1 and 2. Let's go back and dig a little deeper.

How did God create Adam? (Genesis 1:26-27; 2:7)

After God determined that it was not good for man to be alone, what did He instruct Adam to do? (Genesis 2:18-20)

What would Adam have noticed as he named the pairs of animals, male and female?

What does Matthew 6:8 tell us about our needs?

Has God ever made you aware of a need in your life in order to prompt you to ask for His intervention? If so, give an example.

How do you think Adam's realization of his lack affected his gratitude for God's provision?

What are some ways that God has used your husband to provide what was lacking in you?

What are some ways that God has used you to provide what was lacking in him?

Genesis 2:18 begins, "The LORD God said, 'It is not good for the man to be alone. I will make a helper suitable for him." The Hebrew word for helper is "ezer," which means one who comes alongside to aid or assist, to rescue. Ezer appears twenty-one times in the Old Testament. Two times it is used of the woman in Genesis 2, sixteen times it is used of God or Yahweh as helper of His people. The remaining three references appear in the book of the prophets, who used it in reference to military aid. So being an "ezer" is not a junior lackey, but a powerful force to come alongside your husband and serve with him. God created Eve to be

Adam's spiritual, emotional, and physical helper-companion.
How was the way God created Eve different from the way He created
Adam? (Genesis 2:21-22)

The New American Standard Version rightly translates that God "formed"
man (2:7) and "fashioned" woman (2:22). Other translations use the word
for his creation of Eve as "made" rather than "fashioned." Either way, the
words used for how God created Adam and Eve are different.

David Eckman, co-founder and senior lecturer for Kesed Seminars notes
the following:

> Genesis 2 states that God *formed* Adam out of the dust of the
> ground. The Hebrew word is *yatser*, meaning "to fashion as a
> potter." A pot is simple and straightforward. It is usually filled
> with one thing at a time. That nicely illustrates the man as a
> purpose-fulfiller. In a sense, a man is focused upon purposes,
> and when he is pursuing the purpose, he is filled with that one
> thing.
>
> The word for the fashioning of the woman is *banah*, used for
> making palaces, a temple, or forms of art. It implies that the
> woman was meant not only to be a companion, but an
> aesthetic work. Part of the creative work of God is that this
> aesthetic work would have the capacity to sustain her own
> beauty. Researchers tell us that one out of ten men are color-
> blind, while one out of two hundred women are color-blind.
> That implies that God built into women the capacity to be
> aesthetically sensitive.[1]

What does this tell you about the intentionality of God to form and fashion man and woman differently?

> Did you know that every cell in a man's body is different from every cell in a woman's body? That makes millions of inherent differences. The chemicals flowing through our bodies are different. Our muscle structure is different. Even our immune systems are different! Because a woman has two X chromosomes, she actually has a stronger immune system than a man. Women are stronger than men at conception. Few baby girls die before and after birth....Men have almost one million more red blood cells in every drop of blood than women do....Men have an average of one-and-a-half gallons of blood flowing through their bodies, while women only have four-fifths of a gallon. Meanwhile, 40 percent of a man's body weight is muscle while only 20 percent of a woman's body weight is muscle. And men's skin is thicker and bones heavier.[2]

Yes, God created men and women to be different, and we can celebrate those differences! However, what is one aspect of our beings that are the same? (Genesis 1:26-27)

What does it mean to you that your husband was created in the image of God? How does it affect the way you view him? Treat him?

What was God's estimation about what He had made on the first 5 days of creation? (Genesis 1:4, 10, 12, 18, 21, 25)

What was God's estimation about His creation of man and woman on the sixth day of creation? (Genesis 1:31)

What does Genesis 2:25 tell us about both the man and the woman?

Naked obviously means physically naked, but what does it mean to be emotionally naked? To be spiritually naked?

What are some ways that you are emotionally naked with your husband and he with you?

What are some ways that you are spiritually naked with your husband and he with you?

What are some ways that you can make your husband feel safe to be spiritually and emotionally naked before you?

What are some ways that your husband can make you feel safe to be spiritually and emotionally naked before him?

How does being spiritually and emotionally naked with your husband affect your enjoyment of being physically naked with him?

I encourage you to discuss these last five questions with your husband.

Record Adam's first recorded words in Genesis 2:23. Isn't it amazing that man's first recorded words were a love poem about his wife?

Throughout Song of Solomon, we'll see that both the man and the woman compare physical attribute to agricultural and botanical imagery such as flocks, herds, shepherds, horses and vineyards. That might seem a bit odd in our culture, but not to them in their agrarian culture. The imagery of the Song veils the eroticism in beauty and modesty. Physical intimacy between a husband and wife is not for public view, but the Song of Solomon gives us a peek into what it should look like.

List any analogies the couple uses to describe their physical features in Song of Solomon 1. I would suggest using a certain color marker to highlight these throughout the book as we move along.

Go back through Song of Solomon 1 and list all the ways the five senses are engaged.

Sight

Smell

Touch

Hearing

Taste

What does this tell you about how romantic love affects all of your senses?

Let me end our reflection of the creation of man and woman in Genesis chapters 1 and 2 with this quote from author Stephen Schwamback:

> Anybody who has ever experienced great lovemaking instinc-
> tively knows the truth: Sex is too good to have just happened.
> It didn't evolve as the result of some cosmic accident. Some-
> thing this exquisite had to have been lovingly, brilliantly,
> creatively designed.
>
> If an atheist ever comes up to you and demands proof that
> there is a God, all you have to answer is one word: "Sex." Give
> him a day to think about it. If at the end of that day he
> remains unconvinced, then he has just revealed far more
> about his sex life—or lack thereof—than he ever intended!
>
> God created sex. Doesn't that tell you a lot about who God
> really is? Among other things, it tells you that He is ingenious. [3]

How will you let your husband know that you are attracted to him and desire him physically this week? (If you are doing this study in a group, this is one answer you do not need to share. But don't leave it blank!)

How does the Shulammite contrast the heat of the scorning sun in 1:5-7 to the shade of Solomon's love in 2:3?

The Bible often compares shade or the shadow of a tree or a bird's wing to "protection." It arises from the simple analogy of shade under a tree proving protection from the sun, or shade of the wings of a bird providing protection of its young.

What do the following tell you about the shade or protection that God provides?

Psalm 91:1

Psalm 121:5-6

Isaiah 25:4

How is your husband's love like shade from life's glaring sun?

In Song of Solomon 2:4, the Shulammite says, "His banner over me is love."

What do the following references teach us about how banners were used in the Old Testament? *(A banner is sometimes referred to as a "standard.")*

Psalm 20:5

Numbers 1:52

Exodus 17:15

Isaiah 30:17

What new insight do you have for the poetic symbolism of the Shulammite's words, "His banner over me is love?"

A banner in Solomon's day would most often have had a symbol on it to show who or what it represented. This is much like a football banner that would bear the symbol of a mascot, or a flag the symbol of its country. If you had a banner that represented your marriage, what would it look like?

The Shulammite cries out in 2:5, "Strengthen me with raisins cakes, refresh me with apples, for I am weak with love." Look up these additional references to being strengthened with raisin cakes.

1 Samuel 25:18

1 Samuel 30:9-12

2 Samuel 16:1

How would Solomon have interpreted the Shulammite's desire for raisin cakes? Do you think it would make him smile? Laugh? Get excited?

The Shulammite said that she was "weak with love." When you were dating your husband, did you ever feel "weak with love" or "distracted" from your every day tasks? If so, explain.

What impacted you most in *Lovestruck* Chapter 2?

What impacted you most in *Lovestruck* Bible Study Guide Lesson 2?

Reflect

When you were dating your husband, or perhaps even before you were dating him, did you ever drive by where he lived, worked, or played like the Shulammite walked by Solomon's field?

Did you ever go to a place where you knew he would be such as a ball field, a work place, or a party? If so, why did you do that?

What feelings stirred in your heart as you "just so happened" to see him?

The Shulammite took a special interest in the sheep just to catch a glimpse of Solomon. When you were dating your husband, did you take a special interest in something that interested him? If so, what was it?

What interests do you and your husband share today? How do these shared interests deepen your friendship?

The Shulammite confided in her friends. Who was the one person you confided in about your feelings for your husband when you were dating?

What about this friend made her trustworthy to confide in her?
If you are doing this study in a group, this would be a fun reflection to share.

The Shulammite dreamed about the day she and Solomon could be physically intimate. When you were dating, did you daydream about making love to your husband?

Solomon longed to look into the Shulammite's eyes. Do you remember the first time you really looked into your husband's eyes? Explain how you felt.

Lesson Three

Little Foxes and Pesky Fears

Let's continue noting the analogies the couple used to describe each other's physical features. What analogies or comparison did they use to describe one another in Song of Solomon 2? I would suggest using a certain color marker to highlight these throughout the book as we move along.

Go back through Song of Solomon 2 and list all the ways the five senses are engaged to describe romantic love and sexual desire.

Sight:

Smell:

Touch:

Hearing:

Taste:

In 2:8-15, Solomon takes the initiative in their relationship. He bounds over the hills, goes to her home, and calls her out from hiding. In what ways did your husband take the initiative in the dating days?

How did it make you feel to be pursued?

Song of Solomon 2 has one sentence that has been eating away at me...and eating away at vineyards for centuries.

> Catch for us the foxes,
> the little foxes
> that ruin the vineyards,
> our vineyards that are in bloom. (2:15)

We're going to devote the remainder of this lesson to those pesky little foxes, and a lot of powerful Scripture. You might need to stretch this lesson out over a few days.

Look up the following verses and note what Solomon said about some of the little foxes that can destroy a marriage.

Proverbs 3:27

Proverbs 3:30

Proverbs 12:18

Proverbs 16:28

Proverbs 18:13

Proverbs 21:19

Proverbs 21:23

Proverbs 27:15

List a few more little foxes that you've seen creep into marriages.

Read the following verses and note ways to avoid the little foxes.

Proverbs 4:23-27

Proverbs 13:3

Proverbs 15:1

Proverbs 15:28

Proverbs 17:14

Proverbs 24:3-4

I hope you're not too tired to look up a few more verses.

Look up these the New Testament verses to identity a few of the little foxes that can sneak in and wreak havoc on a marriage.

1 Corinthians 7:5

Ephesians 4:26-27

Ephesians 4:32

Ephesians 5:33

Sometimes it is difficult for us to recognize the little foxes and where they came from. Read the following verses and see what you can learn about how to detect the trouble spots.

Proverbs 1:7

Proverbs 2:1-6

Proverbs 8:33-34

Colossians 2:2-3

James 1:5-8

What does Proverbs 14:1 tell us about the wise woman?

What are some ways that you, a wise woman, can keep the "little foxes" from stealing the fruit of your marriage?

Perhaps there are some foxes already wreaking havoc? What do you think you need to do to drive them away?

The Shulammite felt panic at the beginning of Song of Solomon 3. I don't know about you, but I had more than a few worries before Steve and I were married. My parents had a tumultuous relationship, and I worried about how two people who supposedly loved each other in the beginning could so dislike each other years later. *Could that happen to us?* I wondered.

What do the following verses tell us about what to do when we are afraid or worried about our marriages?

Psalm 56:3-4

Isaiah 41:10,13

Psalm 55:22

Matthew 6:34

Proverbs 3:5-6

Philippians 4:6-7

What is the promise of Isaiah 26:3?

If you are worried about your marriage or your man, prayer is the most effective weapon you have to combat the fear. What is the promise of James 5:16b?

What impacted you most in *Lovestruck* Chapter 3?

What impacted you most in *Lovestruck* Bible Study Guide Lesson 3?

Reflect

Recall the day your husband proposed to you. If you are in a group, share!

What did it mean to you to be engaged?

What were some little foxes that you noticed during your dating days? Did you deal with them, or ignore them like most of us did?

Are there any little foxes in your marriage today?

How are you dealing with them?

What fears did you have before your wedding day?

The Shulammite had a bit of a panic attack at the opening of Chapter 4. Did you and your husband-to-be ever have an argument that made you wonder if you had lost him? Explain.

How did you resolve your fears?

Lesson Four

SAYING "I DO" & MEANING "I WILL"

In *Lovestruck* Chapter 4, we looked at the difference between a contract and a covenant. If you think of a marriage as a legal contract between two people, then it's not so special after all. There is a saying, "Contracts are made to be broken." We certainly see that in our culture today. "Until death do us part" has become, "until it gets too difficult and I don't feel in-love with you any longer."

Let's take a deeper look at the difference between a contract and a covenant.

Define the word *contract*.

List contracts that you have or have had over the years? Example: cell phone, house loan, etc.

Were they business agreements or relational agreements?

A contract ends if one party refuses to supply the service or the other party refuses to make the payment. Or it could be that one party doesn't need the service, job, or product, etc. any longer.

List any contracts you have ended. How easy or difficult was it to end the contract?

What happens if you do not hold up your end of a contract, such as neglecting to pay your bill?

Now let's look at a covenant. Define the word *covenant*. If you have a Bible dictionary, use that definition.

In Chapter 4 we saw that marriage is not simply a contract between two people, but a covenant between a husband, wife, and God. The Biblical words most often translated "covenant" in the Bible are *berit* in the Old Testament, (appearing about 280 times) and *diatheke* in the New Testament (appearing about 33 times). In the Old Testament, covenant refers to two or more parties bound together. The word *berit* comes from the root word, "to cut." To make a covenant literally means, "to cut a covenant," however, that doesn't mean that blood is always involved.

What was the sign of the covenant between God and the male Israelites? (Genesis 17:10-14)

In the Bible, there are vertical and horizontal covenants. Read the following verses about God's vertical covenant with Abraham: Genesis 12:1-3; Genesis 15:1-21.

What was the sign of this covenant? (Genesis 17:10-13)

Following God's covenant with Abraham, God renewed His covenant with the Israelite nation with Moses and David. We're not going to study those covenants in this lesson, but know that they are not new covenants, but a continuation and expansion of His covenant with Abraham. Moses' covenant with God included the Ten Commandments that he received on Mount Sinai.

Now let's look at God's New Covenant through Jesus Christ. What do you learn about the New Covenant from these verses?

Jeremiah 31:31-34

Matthews 26:28

Hebrews 9:15

What is the sign of this covenant?

There were also horizontal covenants between two or more people in the Bible. What do you learn about horizontal covenants from the following?

The covenant between David and Samuel. (1 Samuel 18:1-4)

The covenant between Ruth and Naomi. (Ruth 1:16-17)

What does Malachi call the wife? The wife of your _____
_____. Malachi 2:14

How does Proverbs 2:17 describe the husband of the wayward woman?

When God made a covenant with man, He often changed their name.

Look up Genesis 17:5,15 and note the name change:

A wife taking her husband's last name is a tradition in our culture. If you are in a group, share your maiden name.

How did you feel about changing your last name?

How does the name change reflect a covenant relationship?

What does it say about your identity?

What is one difference between a covenant between two people and a covenant between man and God? (Numbers 23:19)

Before a couple says their wedding vows to each other, traditionally the pastor will ask them a few questions. It usually goes something like this: "Will you have this man to be your husband, to live together with him in the covenant of marriage? Will you love him, comfort him, honor and keep him, in sickness and in health, and, forsaking all others, be faithful unto him as long as you both shall live?"

The bride answers, "I will." The groom answers, "I will."

The bride and groom aren't making a promise to the pastor who's asking the question. To whom are the bride and groom making this covenant promise? Is this a vertical or horizontal commitment?

After the bride and groom make this covenant promise, they turn to each other and say their vows to one another. Is this a vertical or horizontal commitment?

Just to sum it up: To whom is the vertical commitment?

To whom is the horizontal commitment?

So in essence, marriage vows are not simply between a man and a woman, but between a man, a woman, and God. Read Ecclesiastes 4:12 and note what Solomon said makes a strong relationship. What do the three strands represent?

A covenant marriage is not dependent on whether one party holds up his or her end of the bargain to pay the bills, do the laundry, or mow the lawn. A covenant marriage involves sacrifice. It is more about giving than getting, serving than being served, loving the person whether we feel like he deserves it or not.

Consider the words, "For better or for worse. For richer or for poorer. In sickness and in health. Till death do us part." Do those words sound contractual or covenantal? Explain your answer.

In the New Testament, what did Jesus establish as a sign of the New Covenant? Matthew 26:26-28

What did he tell them to remember every time they ate the bread and drank the wine from that point on? Luke 22:19

When we celebrate communion, or the Lord's Supper, what are we remembering?

The New Covenant accomplished what the Old could not—the removal of sin and cleansing of the conscience (Hebrews 10:2,22). The work of Jesus Christ on the cross thus makes the old covenant "obsolete" (Hebrews 8:13) and fulfills the promise of the prophet Jeremiah.

Every time we celebrate the Lord's Supper by taking communion, we remember God's covenant of salvation through Christ Jesus' finished work on the cross.

Every time we come together sexually, we remember the covenant we made on our wedding day.

This is a lot to learn about covenants, but I want us to grasp the seriousness of it.

What is the visual sign or symbol of the covenant made with your husband on your wedding day?

What do you hope your husband thinks when he looks at his wedding ring?

Read and record Mark 10:6-9.

The reason to stay married is not because you feel like it. I've had many days when I just didn't feel like being married. I bet you have too. We stay married because we made a covenant before God. Then when we don't feel like staying in it, we ask, "What can we do to fix this? Where can we go for help?"

The sexual attraction and relationship between a husband and wife is an amazingly beautiful creation of God. It is very private, and yet, we can take the time to marvel and ponder His creative genius. I love what the writer of Proverbs had to say:

> Three things are too wonderful for me;
>   four I do not understand:
> the way of an eagle in the sky,
>   the way of a serpent on a rock,
> the way of a ship on the high seas,
>   and the way of a man with a virgin.
> Proverbs 30:18-19 (ESV)

Yep, the fourth was almost just too amazing to try and figure out.
I'm proud of you for sticking with this study.

What impacted you most in *Lovestruck* Chapter 4?

What impacted you most in the *Lovestruck* Bible Study Guide Lesson 4?

Reflect

How long did it take to plan your wedding?

What were some elements that you really wanted to include?

Did anything unexpected happen at your wedding or reception?

In what ways did your wedding mirror your intention of having a marriage that would last a lifetime?

How is a wedding an act of faith?

What part does faith play in your marriage today?

Recall your wedding day. If you are doing the study in a group, consider bringing your wedding pictures to share.

What was the highlight of your wedding day?

    Who attended?

    Who was in the wedding party?

    What did their presence mean to you?

    What did the guests' presence signify to you?

In what kind of car did you drive away from you wedding? Rented? Decorated? Borrowed?

In addition to the guests that were present at your wedding, how was God's presence reflected?

If you wrote your wedding vows, consider finding them and reading them again. If your pastor used a standard version, you can probably find a similar version on the Internet. Print out a copy and remind each other of your commitment.

Lesson Five

Unlocking the Secret Garden

Go through Song of Solomon 4 and list the ways the five senses are engaged on their first night together as husband and wife.

Sight

Smell

Touch

Hearing

Taste

Sex was part of Creator-God's divine plan for husband and wife. What did He say about the way He fashioned man and wife to become one flesh? Genesis 1:31a

God doesn't simply allow sex in marriage, He encourages it! What do you learn from Proverbs 5:19 and Deuteronomy 24:5?

What was God's first directive to Adam and Eve? (Genesis 1:28)

Review God's directive for a husband and wife in Genesis 2:24.

What do you think it means to become "one flesh"?

Tim Keller wrote,

> "To call the marriage 'one flesh,' then, means that sex is understood as both a sign of that personal, legal union and a means to accomplish it. The Bible says don't unite with someone physically unless you are also willing to unite with the person emotionally, personally, socially, economically, and legally. Don't become physically naked and vulnerable to the other person without becoming vulnerable in every other way, because you have given up your freedom and bound yourself in marriage. Then, once you have given yourself in marriage, sex is a way of maintaining and deepening that union as the years go by." [4]

What does the writer of Hebrews tell us about the marriage bed? (Hebrews 13:4) Read this from various Bible translations to gain further insight. *(Biblehub.com and Biblegateway.com are two good resources when comparing translations.)*

Define the word "honor."

How does that apply to marriage?

Define the words "undefiled" and "pure."

How do those words apply to marriage?

One way we keep the marriage bed undefiled is by being sexually faithful to our spouse. What do the following verses teach us about sex outside the confines of marriage?

1 Corinthians 6:18

1 Thessalonians 4:3-8

Proverbs 6:20-35

Hebrews 13:4

What does 1 Corinthians 6:17-20 teach us about what happens in the sexual union between a man and a woman, whether they are married or not?

According to that verse, why is sex outside of marriage so dangerous?

C.S. Lewis likened sex without marriage to tasting food without swallowing and digesting it. Explain what you think he meant by that analogy.

Make a list of 5-10 steps that lead up to an affair. I'll get you started.

1. Flirting with someone of the opposite sex.

2. Confiding with someone of the opposite sex about marital problems.

3.

4.

5.

6.

7.

8.

9.

10.

List 5-10 boundaries that help create a protective hedge around a marriage to prevent an affair. I'll get you started.

1. Avoid spending time alone with a person of the opposite sex.

2. Have an accountability partner and admit if you are attracted to someone other than your husband.

3.

4.

5.

6.

7.

8.

9.

10.

The word holy often means, "set apart for special use." In light of that definition, how is sex between a husband and a wife "holy"?

God meant for sex between a husband and wife to be pleasurable. Think of all that He put into fashioning a husband's and wife's body for that very reason. All you need to make a baby is a receptive egg and a determined sperm. God fashioned much more than was necessary for that to occur.

List a few body parts that God fashioned that are simply for sexual pleasure.

What does James 1:17 tell us about God's good gifts?

Pause and thank God for the way He crafted your and your husband's body for physical intimacy. Write out a prayer of gratitude.

We looked at 1 Corinthians 7:2-5 in Lesson 5. Let's look at it again. To whom does the wife's body belong?

To whom does the husband's body belong?

How is this opposite to what our current culture teaches?

This was new teaching for Paul's day. Nothing like this had ever been taught before. In Bible days, women were treated as property. It was expected for men to have a wife for procreation of legitimate heirs, and sexual partners outside of marriage for pleasure. Explain what made Paul's teaching radically different.

How does 1 Corinthians 7:2-5 put men and women on equal footing in regard to sex in marriage?

Does 1 Corinthians 7:2-5 assume that a woman desires sex?

In Song of Solomon 4, notice how Solomon touched his bride with his words before he touched her with his hands. How do well-spoken words play a major role in sexual desire and fulfillment in marriage?

How do harsh words create a barrier to sexual intimacy?

Read and record Proverbs 18:21.

How does that verse apply to sexual intimacy? How do words bring life or death to your and your husband's enjoyment of sex?

It's been said that when it comes to sex, women want gentleness and men want responsiveness. How do we see that played out in Song of Solomon 4?

How was he gentle?

How was she responsive?

How do you usually respond to your husband during lovemaking?

How do you think he would like for you to respond?

Solomon compares his wife's sexuality to a spring, a fountain, and well of flowing water streaming down from Lebanon (4:12,15). How do these verses relate to Solomon's words in Proverbs 5:15?

The Hebrew word used for "cistern" is *bor*, which is a receptacle for holding water from rainfall or from an external spring. Sometimes they were dug out of the earth or rock. During the rainy season, the cistern would fill, and then the water would be used during the dry summer season. These cisterns were usually large pits, but sometimes were extensive vaults, open only by a small mouth. The mouth was closed with a large flat stone, over which sand was spread to prevent easy discovery.[5]

Wells, or the Hebrew word *beer*, were different in that the water rose up from the bottom. Typically, both cisterns and wells were privately owned.

How does the idea of wells and cisterns being privately owned reflect the exclusivity of sexual relations between a husband and wife?

Why do you think Solomon compares sex between a husband and wife to various images of water?

What does this tell you about how sex with you affects your husband's heart and soul?

I hope I haven't worn you out by talking about the word "covenant," but let's touch on it one more time. In the Old Testament, there were often ceremonies to renew covenants. We saw how Jesus instructed us to remember the New Covenant every time we take the bread and wine of communion. How is making love to your husband like renewing the marriage covenant each time you come together?

In closing, let me share words from Tim Keller that might be a new thought for you…your sexual relationship with your husband reflects of the glorious relationship of the Trinity—a taste of what you will experience when you are in Their presence face-to-face.

> "Sex is glorious. We would know that even if we didn't have the Bible. Sex leads us to words of adoration—it literally evokes shouts of joy and praise. Through the Bible, we know why this is true. John 17 tells us that from all eternity, the Father, Son, and Holy Spirit have been adoring and glorifying each other, living in high devotion to each other, pouring love and joy into one another's hearts continually (John 1:18; 17:5, 21-25). Sex between a man and a woman points to the love between the Father and the Son (1 Corinthians 11:3). It is a reflection of the joyous self-giving and pleasure of love within the very life of the triune God.
>
> Sex is glorious not only because it reflects the joy of the Trinity, but also because it points to the eternal delight of soul that we will have in heaven, in our loving relationships with God and one another. Romans 7:1 tells us that the best marriages are pointers to the deep, infinitely fulfilling and final union we will have with Christ in love."[6]

What impacted you most in *Lovestruck* Chapter 5?

What impacted you most in *Lovestruck* Bible Study Guide Lesson 5?

What was the best part of your honeymoon?

If you are in a group, share where you went, how long you stayed, and if you have ever returned to the same place.

Did you communicate with anyone back home while you were away on your honeymoon?

Thinking back on Solomon's words to the Shulammite on their honeymoon, what is the most endearing compliment your husband has ever given you? How did it make you feel?

What do you think is the most endearing compliment you have ever given your husband? You might want to ask him that question.

How has your times of physical intimacy changed from the first time you came together as husband and wife?

The Shulammite wore a large necklace on her wedding day (4:4). Did you wear a special piece of jewelry?

Did you enjoy introducing your man as "your husband" when you were first married?

Did you practice writing your new name when you were first married? Take a moment and write out your full married name, beginning with Mrs.

When was the last time you told your man that you're glad that he's your husband?

Lesson Six

Trouble in Paradise
. . . .

Wow, what a contrast between Song of Solomon 4 and 5! How does the Beloved's response to her new husband in Chapter 5 differ from her responses to him in 1:2-4,12-14,16; 2:3-7,16-17?

About how long did it take for you to have a similar response to your husband's advances once you were married?

How does her response contradict what we learned in 1 Corinthians 7:1-5?

According to 1 Corinthians 7:1-5, when is it acceptable to deprive one another of sexual intimacy? Fill in the blanks

Except perhaps _____ _____

For a _____

So that you may_____ _____ _____ _____.

And why should you come back together after the time of mutual consent? (1:5)

After the devil tempted Jesus in the wilderness for 40 days, he left. When was he planning on returning to tempt him again? (Luke 4:13)

The Greek word translated "opportune" is *kairos*. It is derived from *kara* ("head") referring to things "coming to a head" to take full–advantage of. *Karios* is "the suitable time, the right moment, a favorable moment."

How does deprivation of sexual intimacy give the devil an "opportune time" to attack you or your husband?

As a wife, how can we make sure the devil does not have this particular opportune time to attack our marriages? I'm not trying to insult your intelligence by asking this simple question. Sometimes we just need to write it down in black and white.

We must always make sure that we never use withholding sex as a punishment for bad behavior or engaging in sex as a reward for good behavior. Sex is never to be used to manipulate or control.

Let's talk about what love looks like according to 1 Corinthians 13:1-13. List the attributes of love in theses verses that are actions or acts of the will.

List the attributes of love in these verses that are emotions or feelings.

What does it say to you that so many of the attributes of love are actions or decisions, rather than emotions or feelings?

Based on this passage, can you love someone even when you don't necessarily feel like it? Explain.

The most poignant part of Song of Solomon 5 was how quickly the Shulammite made the first move toward reconciliation, and the ease in which Solomon forgave her. We'll look at forgiveness in the next lesson. For now, let's focus on the Shulammite's quick move toward reconciliation.

Tommy Nelson wrote:
"All couples fight. Good couples fight clean. Bad couples fight dirty. Good couples press to a resolution. Bad couples press for a victory. When one person wins, both lose. For good couples, a conflict will expose character. For bad couples, a conflict will expose immaturity…While conflict is inevitable, resolution must be intentional."[8]

One of the key stumbling blocks to making the first move toward reconciliation is pride. Pride says, "I'm right and you're wrong. Period."

Define the word *pride*.

Being proud of someone for his or her character or accomplishments is not a bad thing. Being filled with self-pride is. Being prideful is to have an inflated sense of one's own worth or personal status that leads to a sense of superiority over others.

How does God feel about self-pride?
    Psalm 10:4

    Proverbs 8:13

    Proverbs 16:5

    James 4:6

Note the sins with which pride is listed. What does this teach you about the seriousness of pride? (Mark 7:21-23)

What do you learn from the following verses about pride?
    Proverbs 16:18

    Proverbs 29:23

    1 Corinthians 13:4

Do you think these verses apply to marriage?

How does pride manifest itself in marriage?

What are seven things that God hates? (Proverbs 6:16-19) How is pride at the center of each one?

The words "haughty eyes" are particularly telling. The Hebrew word for haughty is "ruwm" and means "to rise, to be high, to be lofty," and "to be exalted." Haughty eyes are eyes that look down on other people. How does that relate to couples when they have an argument or disagreement?

Where do you think pride comes from?

Pride is often called the first sin. How did the serpent's temptation appeal to Adam's and Eve's sense of pride? (Genesis 3:1-5)

How does 1 John 2:16 reflect what happened in the Garden as recorded in Genesis 3:1-5?

The opposite of pride is humility. Define *humility*.

How does Proverbs 11:2 contrast pride and humility?

How did Jesus humble Himself? (Philippians 2:5-11) What was the end result?

Pride can be a roadblock standing in the way or forgiveness and reconciliation. Let's take a closer look at those two words.

Look up and define the word *reconciliation*.

Look up and define the word *forgiveness*.

How are they different? How are they similar?

What do the following verses teach about the importance of reconciliation?

      Matthew 5:25-26

      Colossians 3:13

      Matthew 18:21-35

I'm so proud of how the Shulammite made the first step toward reconciliation. (There, I wanted to use the word, proud, in a positive way.) I want to emulate that quality in my marriage. I know you do too.

What impacted you most is *Lovestruck* Chapter 6?

What impacted you most in the *Lovestruck* Bible Study Guide Lesson 6?

Reflect

What are some typical things you and your husband argue about?

What are some ways that you know you hurt your husband? Example: cold shoulder, snarky attitude, withholding affection?

Are you holding any grudges against him for past failures?

What do you need to do with your list of offenses?

Do you need to make the first move and ask for his forgiveness for a past action or attitude?

Lesson Seven

This Is My Lover, This Is My Friend

I'm so thankful for the Shulammite's friends who brought her back to her senses.

When the joy of love tarnishes wonder, rusty words often rise to the surface. While the Shulammite had given her husband the cold shoulder, her words warmed her heart toward her man. She began changing her attitude toward him when she changed her words about him.

What do the following Proverbs teach you about the words we speak?

Proverbs 12:25

Proverbs 11:25

Proverbs 15:1

Proverbs 15:4

Proverbs 16:24

What did Solomon say about a wife's negative words?

Proverbs 19:13

Proverbs 21:9,19

Proverbs 27:15-16

What did Solomon say about a wife's positive words?

Proverbs 12:4

Proverbs 31:10,26,28,29

Which woman do you think your husband would say you most resemble?

As a wife, we have a choice every day to be an encourager or discourager our husbands. Define the word *encourage*.

Define the word *discourage*.

What does the Bible say about the importance of encouraging one another?

1 Thessalonians 5:11

Hebrews 3:13

Hebrews 10:24-25

Ephesians 4:29

Romans 14:19

These verses are aimed at Christians encouraging one another in the faith. If we are called to encourage other brothers and sisters in Christ, how much more are we called to encourage the brother in Christ that we call husband!

Read, record, and memorize Proverbs 18:21. (I personally like the ESV translation of this verse.)

How do positive words bring life to a marriage?

How do negative words bring death to a marriage?

How do encouraging, loving words affect the quality of sexual intimacy in a marriage?

How do discouraging, hurtful words affect the quality of sexual intimacy in a marriage?

Let's look at an example of how a wife used her words to discourage her husband. At one time, the Ark of the Covenant had been captured by the Philistines, and later relocated in Baalah in Judah. David had his heart set on bringing it back to the City of David. In the procession bringing the

Ark back to it's rightful place, David, dressed in a linen ephod (think modern-day undershirt) danced before the Lord with all his might.

How did David's wife, Michal, discourage him from praising God? (2 Samuel 6:16-20)

What was David and God's response to her? (2 Samuel 6:21-23)

We don't know if God closed her womb, or if David never slept with her again. Either way, it was not a positive outcome for Michal.

What conclusion can you draw from this scenario about the power of a woman's words to build up or tear down her marriage and her man?

How do rusty (negative) words affect a couple's sex life?

One of the most effective ways to maintain intimacy in marriage happens way before a couple crawls between the sheets. It starts with what happens between the lips…the words that come out of our mouths. We see this throughout the entire Song. Sure, we see their passion compared to various fruits, but the fruit of our lips is the beginning and ending point of any relationship.

In the Lesson 5, we looked at what the Bible said about "honoring" the marriage bed and keeping it undefiled or pure. Now, let's look at that word *honor*.

Define the words *honor* and *respect*.

Some sources say honor and respect are synonyms. You can't have one without the other. How are they similar?

The Hebrew word used for *honor* in the Old Testament is *"kabad"* (Exodus 20:12). It means, "to be heavy, weighty and glorious." The Greek word used for *honor* in the New Testament is *"timao"*. It means "to estimate, to fix the value of, to revere or venerate" (Ephesians 6:2).

With that in mind, what do the following verses teach us about honor and respect in marriage? If you have access to the Amplified translation of the Bible which defines and expounds on certain words, see what it has to say.

Romans 12:10

1 Peter 3:7

Ephesians 5:33

So far, how have we seen Solomon honor the Shulammite?

So far, how have we seen the Shulammite honor her husband?

Dr. Gary Smalley notes that the two most important principles that keep a couple in love and in a mutually satisfying relationship are honoring your spouse and keeping your relationship secure.[9]

Give three examples of ways a wife might dishonor her husband.

Give three examples of ways a husband might dishonor his wife.

Give three examples of ways a husband might honor his wife.

Give three examples of ways a wife might honor her husband.

(These might be four questions that you want to discuss with your spouse.)

Philippians 2:3 takes it one step further. Look up the verse and answer this question: What are ways that you can honor your husband above yourself, or put his needs above your own?

What impacted you the most from *Lovestruck* Chapter 7?

What impacted you the most from the *Lovestruck* Bible Study Guide Lesson 7?

Reflect

Would your husband say that you're his greatest critic or his greatest cheerleader?

Do you think your husband receives more or less admiration and appreciation from you or from co-workers and business partners?

When was the last time you told your husband that he was a wonderful_____? What do you think he would love for you to put in that blank?

What are five of your husband's physical features that you admire most?

Let's follow the Shulammite's lead and fill in the following. "When I first fell in love with my husband, I thought he looked like a _____." Put the name of an animal in the blank. No matter what he looks like today, when he looks in the mirror, he still sees that same man.

Take some time to write out a few compliments that you will shower on our husband during the course of this study. Then go back and check them off once you've actually done it.

Lesson Eight

Forgiveness and the Dance of Two Camps

In Song of Solomon 5, we saw how quickly the Shulammite took the first step toward reconciliation and restoration. In Song of Solomon 6, we saw how quickly Solomon forgave her.

In the course of this love song, there is no mention of bitterness, resentment, or paying back hurt for hurt. Only grace.

What do the following verses teach about paying back hurt for hurt?
1 Thessalonians 5:15

1 Peter 2:21-23

Romans 12:17-21

What do the following verses teach about the importance of forgiving others?
Colossians 3:13

Mark 11:25

Ephesians 4:31-32

How did Jesus forgive us?

How does Jesus continue to forgive us?

How does this apply to your marriage?

Going back to 1 Corinthians 13:5, what does love NOT do? How does this apply to your marriage?

Forgiveness is a decision and can happen in a moment. However, reconciliation from bigger offenses beyond the garden variety may take a bit more time. For reconciliation to occur, the offender needs to confess or admit that what he or she did was wrong and be truly repentant. However, for forgiveness to occur, neither is required.

You can forgive someone without having reconciliation. In some cases, that is advisable. However, you cannot have reconciliation without forgiveness to maintain a strong, ever-deepening marriage.

What does Ephesians 4:26 tell you about the urgency for reconciliation?

You might not be able to settle a conflict before you go to bed, but the key is to set aside a time to talk about it quickly, and avoid allowing an emotional splinter to fester.

Now let's get practical. What does that look like in a marriage?

Notice this verse doesn't say, "Do not be angry." However, it does say "Be angry, but do not sin." Even Jesus got angry, but He did not sin (Hebrews 4:15; 2 Corinthians 5:21). What do the following verses tell you about when Jesus was angry?

Matthew 21:12-13; John 2:13-19; Mark 11:15-18 (The same story is in these three Gospel accounts. You can just pick one.)

Mark 3:5 (note that Jesus' anger was laced with grief)

Jesus got angry at the things that angered God. We humans tend to get angry at the things that offend our pride or self-centeredness. Righteous anger is governed by love. Self-righteous anger is governed by self.

The New Testament uses two Greek words translated *anger*. One means "passion, energy" and the other means "agitated, boiling." "Biblically, anger is God-given energy intended to help us solve problems."[10] Examples of righteous anger in the Bible do not involve self-defense, but a defense of others or of a principle.

When does anger become a sin? (If you are doing this in a group, there might be several different answers.)

What does James 1:19 tell us about anger?

How does being slow to anger reflect God's grace?

My friend Tracie Miles outlines seven ways to know when our anger is sinful. Look up the following verses to gain insight.

1. When the reason for being angry is selfishly motivated. James 1:20 (this one we just answered above)

2. When being angry is not glorifying God or defending His name. 1 Corinthians 10:31

3. When anger goes on for so long, that it gives the devil a foothold in your heart. Ephesians 4:26b-27

4. When anger is so volatile, that it begins to bring emotional or physical harm to others. Psalm 37:8

5. When anger causes us to hold grudges against people with the intent of making them suffer. Ephesians 4:31

6. When anger makes us unwilling to forgive, and consumes us with revenge. Ephesians 4:32

7. When we hold on so tightly to our anger that we begin to feel depressed and irritable, often erupting over small insignificant things.[11] Hebrews 12:15

What are we to do with anger? (Colossians 3:8)

Bottom line, we're all going to get angry with our spouses. That's just part of the package. What we do with that anger will make the difference between bitter resentment that poisons the relationship or forgiveness and reconciliation that sweetens it.

Can you think of a time when you and your husband experienced resolution and reconciliation that sweetened your relationship?

Can you think of a time when you or your husband held on to anger and it harmed your relationship?

We cannot completely forget an offense. Don't you wish we could push a delete button and it would be wipe away from our memory?! Biblically speaking, to "forget" an offense means that we are no longer going to act on it. We're going to put the offense behind us and move on.

What does Philippians 3:13 tell us to do with past offenses?

What are a few of the offenses that Paul had to leave behind?
(2 Corinthians 11:23-28)

What do the following verses tell us about what God does with our sin when we are truly repentant and ask Him to forgive us?

1 John 1:9

Isaiah 43:25-26

Hebrews 10:17

When the Bible says that God forgets, that means He is no longer going to act on the offense. With that in mind, what does "forgive and forget" mean to you?

What happens in our hearts and ultimately our marriage when we choose not to forgive? (Hebrews 12:15—We've already looked at this verse, but it's worth looking at it again.)

What sort of fruit grows from a bitter root?

How does unforgiveness affect sexual intimacy and emotional closeness?

I love how Solomon and the Shulammite refer to sitting under the apple tree in several places through the love song. When we have unforgiveiness in marriage, the sweet apple tree becomes a bitter crabapple tree…and there's nothing sweet about it.

Someone once said, "The first to apologize is the bravest. The first to forgive is the strongest. The first to forget is the happiest." The Shulammite sought forgiveness. Solomon never mentioned it again.

What impacted you the most from *Lovestruck* Chapter 8?

What impacted you the most from the *Lovestruck* Bible Study Guide Lesson 8?

Reflect

What was the subject of the very first argument you and your husband ever had?

How quickly did you reconcile?

Who made the first move?

I loved how Solomon reassured the Shulammite of his love when she came to him in repentance. Think back to a time your husband asked you to forgive him. How did you reassure him of your love?

Think back to a time when your husband forgave you. How did he reassure you of his love?

Is there something that you need to forgive your husband for today? Jot it down.

Is there something that you need to ask your husband to forgive you for today? Jot it down.

In Song of Solomon 6:10, the Shulammite's friends mentioned that she "appears like the dawn, fair as the moon, bright as the sun, majestic as the stars." How does the giving and receiving of forgiveness brightens one's face and countenance?

Have you ever noticed the face of an angry bitter person? How would you describe it?

How is the appearance of a vengeful bitter person different from a grace-filled, forgiving person?

Lesson Nine

The Ageless Beauty of Committed Love

In The Song of Solomon 7, the couple is in the bedroom...again. The Bible reminds us through the words of Solomon and the Shulammite that God created our bodies to enjoy sex between a husband and wife.

Go back through the Song of Solomon 7 and list all the ways the five senses are engaged.

Sight

Smell

Touch

Hearing

Taste

What phrases in Song of Solomon 7 let you know that both Solomon and the Shulammite are enjoying each other...delighting in each other?

Adam and Eve had it made, to say the least. They had complete union and communion with God and each other. But we know how that turned out. They disobeyed God's one restriction, and their freedom turned into bondage. Sin entered the world, and with it, the marriage relationship became one of shame, control, manipulation, and regret.

However, God did not leave man to flounder in the darkness of a fallen world. He gave us the ultimate role model of what a marriage can be and an example of how restoration should be…Himself. He showed us how to have a covenant relationship that lasts a lifetime and how to sacrificially serve one another.

By what name is God referred to in Isaiah 54:5?

What did God tell the Israelites in Ezekiel 16:8?

What did God do to initiate His relationship with His Bride? (Ezeikiel16:8-14).

Ezekiel is an allegory of what God did for His Bride, Israel, and ultimately the Christian church that was grafted in. (See Galatians 3:6-9.)

How is this similar to what Boaz did for Ruth? (Ruth 3:9)

"The spreading of a corner of a man's garment over a woman was symbolic of entering into a marriage covenant. It expressed both protection and intimacy, just as God initiated a relationship with His people and drew them into His divine protection....The words 'entered into a covenant' indicated an unbreakable bond—something that, once enacted, could not be dissolved except at penalty of death. God had forever linked Himself to His Bride!"[12]

How does this reflect the relationship between husband and wife?

In the Old Testament, God is depicted as the husband of His people the Israelites—the Jews. In the New Testament, Jesus Christ is pictured as the Bridegroom of the Church—all who believe in Him as Savior and Lord. Read the following and note any parallel you see between the marriage of Christ and the Church and a husband and wife.

2 Corinthians 11:2

Ephesians 5:21-33

Revelation 19:7

What is expected of both the husband and the wife in these passages? Would you say these actions come naturally? Explain.

I'm going to go out on a limb and think you said that these actions and emotions do not always come naturally. Isn't it wonderful to know that we are not left on our own to have a thriving marriage?

Where does our strength come from?

Psalm 121:1-3

Psalm 28:7

Psalm 18:1-2

And if that's not enough, what kind of power is available to all Christ followers? Ephesians 1:18-21

As we've seen, the marriage between a husband and wife is an earthly example of the relationship between Christ and the Church—you and me. How does the effort you put forth to grow spiritually reflect to the effort you put forth to grow emotionally, physically, and spiritually with your husband?

Sin comes naturally. Sanctified or holy living comes supernaturally. How does that relate to marriage?

In Ephesians 5:32 Paul concludes his comparison of Christ and the Church to the marriage of husband and wife with the words, "this is a profound mystery." The Greek word is *mysterion*. He literally uses the word, *mega-mysterion*. Use a Bible commentary to learn more about what that word means in the original language. Tim Keller calls this: "An extraordinarily great, wonderful and profound truth that can be understood only with the help of God's Spirit."[13] It is like a secret, or better yet, the secret to marriage that Paul is referring to.

In Ephesians 5:25, Paul writes, "Husbands, love your wives just as Christ loved the Church and gave himself up for her." What is he referring to when he says, "gave himself up for her?(Also see Philippians 2:5, Romans 6:5, 2 Peter 1:4.)

How can a husband love his wife in the same manner?

From Philippians 2:5-11, would you say that Jesus gave His life for the Church because He had to or because He wanted to?

What does that attitude tell you about how a husband and wife should serve and love each other?

I love how Paul writes about marriage. It is as if he is saying, "If you don't know what to do to have a great marriage, start here. Do what Jesus did for His Bride."

As Keller said, "So, what do you need to make marriage work? You need to know the secret, the gospel, and how it gives you both the power and the pattern for your marriage. On the other hand, the experience of marriage will unveil the beauty and depths of the gospel to you."[14]

Unpack that statement. Explain what you think Keller means in your own words.

In Song of Solomon 7, we saw a beautiful picture of serving one another in the bedroom. Solomon lovingly knelt in front of his wife and removed her sandals...taking the position of a servant. Let's dig deeper into how we are to serve our husbands and how they are to serve us as well.

The Greek word translated "serve" in the New Testament is *diakoneo*. It means "caring for the needs of others as the Lord guides in an active, practical way."

What do the following verses teach us about serving others? How does each verse relate to marriage?

Proverbs 11:25

2 Corinthians 5:15

Galatians 5:13

1 John 3:18

Philippians 2:3

What does the word "consider" in Philippians 2:3 imply?

What similarities do you see between Romans 15:1-7 and Philippians 2:2-3?

Most of the time when Paul writes about being a servant, he is using the Greek word "doulos," which means bond-servant. In the Old Testament, the Hebrew word with a similar connotation is "ebed." In the Bible, a bondservant is a person who is a slave or servant to another by choice. When a slave was set free, he or she could choose to remain a servant to his or her master.

Exodus 21:5-6 introduces the idea of a bondservant. Describe the process.

When someone committed to become a bondservant of another, how long was the commitment for?

I'm not suggesting that husbands and wives are slaves to one another, but what a beautiful picture of deciding to serve each other for life...not because you have to, but because you want to.

Tim Keller writes in The Meaning of Marriage,
> "The deep happiness that marriage can bring, then, lies on
> the far side of sacrificial service in the power of the Spirit. That
> is, you only discover your own happiness after each of you
> has put the happiness of your spouse ahead of your own, in a
> sustained way, in response to what Jesus has done for you . . .
> It is the joy that comes from giving joy, from loving another
> person in a costly way."[16]

The opposite of a serving-one-another attitude is a self-serving attitude. Read 1 Corinthians 13:4-5 once again and record what loves does and what loves does not do. What does that look like in a marriage relation-ship?

What does James 3:16 teach about self-centeredness? How does self-centeredness create disorder and evil practices? (You might want to look this up in other Bible translations.)

How does Jesus sum up the entire law in Matthew 22:37-40?

How does this relate to your marriage?

The word "neighbor" means "near person." I think this verse can apply not only to those people living in the house beside us, but also to the husband sleeping in the bed next to us.

Self-centeredness is every person's default mode. However, when we come to Christ, we have the power of the Holy Spirit to move us beyond our natural tendencies to make supernatural choices.

How does Jesus' washing the disciples feet, recorded in John 13:1-17, demonstrate the servant attitude we should have toward our spouse, and he toward us?

How does serving one another show humility?

How does serving one another deepen intimacy?

The idea of a wife putting her husband's needs above her own, and a husband putting his wife's needs above his own, does not come naturally. It is only through the power of the Holy Spirit that we can love like Christ. Even with a commitment to do so, it doesn't happen overnight. It takes Bible study, prayer, and practice.

What did Paul pray for us in the following verses?

Philippians 1:9-11

Ephesians 1:17-20

Colossians 2:1-3

Here's what let's do—let's pray each of these prayers for our husbands this week.

What impacted you most in *Lovestruck* Chapter 9?

What impacted you most in the *Lovestruck* Bible Study Guide Lesson 9?

Reflect

What is one time that you served your husband well?

What is one time that your husband served you well?

How would a wife thinking of sex as serving her husband—rather than fulfilling an obligation—change her attitude? (Not that you're that person)

What are five ways that you can serve your husband this week?

Lesson Ten

Keeping Romance Alive with Something Old, Something New

Pray first that God will open your eyes and heart before you begin this lesson. Now that you've prayed, read Ephesians 5:21-33.

How are wives charged to relate to their husbands in Ephesians 5:21-33?

How does verse 5:21 reflect the idea of serving one another as we discussed in Lesson 9?

How is this repeated in Colossians 3:18-19, 1 Peter 3:1-7, and Titus 2:5?

Submission does not mean that women are less than men in any way. Men and women, husbands and wives, are co-heirs with Christ. What does Galatians 3:28 say about the equality of men and women in the eyes of God?

I know I said I was going to limit the commentary in the Bible study, but submission is a touchy subject (no pun intended).

Here's what John Piper says submission is not:

1. Submission is not agreeing on everything, for instance the Christian faith, because the husband in 1 Peter 3:1-6 is an unbeliever.

2. Submission does not mean leaving your brain at the altar, or that the husband works independently from the wife. Leadership doesn't even mean always getting the last word. On a basic level, Piper's wife wrote, "We settled the principle early that if we can't agree, Jonny's going to make the call." However, she admitted that rarely happens.

3. Submission does not mean you do not try to influence your husband, which is the whole point of 1 Peter 3:1-6.

4. Submission is not putting the will of the husband before the will of Christ, (participating in anything illegal or immoral)

5. Submission does not mean the wife gets all of her spiritual strength through her husband.

6. Submission does not mean living or acting in fear.

Submission is not forced control. Never. It does not belittle, discourage, or ignore. I love John Piper's definition of submission in marriage: "Submission is the defined calling of a wife to honor and affirm her husband's leadership, and so help to carry it through according to her gifts." [17]

Back to Ephesians 5:25-28. How are husbands to relate to their wives? What example are they to emulate?

Wives are called to show respect and submit. Husbands are called to give their lives. So who has the harder job?

How is the charge to husbands and wives in Ephesians 5:12-18 a reflection of the gospel?

In light of the fact that the gospel of Jesus Christ is the gospel of grace, how should marriage also reflect that grace?

What is the truth of 1 John 4:19-21?

How can that truth spur us on to love on the days when we really don't feel like it?

How do both the wife submitting to her husband and the husband loving his wife as Christ loved the Church reflect serving one another in love?

How does Paul tell us to walk out the Christian life in the very first sentence of Ephesians 5?

So just as Ephesians 5:21 tells us to submit one to another, Ephesians 5:1-2 tells us to live a life of love—laying down our lives one for another.

How do you think being filled with the Spirit as Paul describes in Ephesians 5:18,and submitting one to another as Paul describes in Ephesians 5:21, are related?

So before Paul gives instructions for how marriage is a reflection of Christ and the Church, he is assuming that the couple is "filled with the Spirit." He doesn't specify any cultural actions or practical applications about submission, but appears to believe that if you're filled with the Holy Spirit, you'll know how to submit to each other in love.

When it comes to love and respect, some say, "when my husband starts loving me like Jesus loves the Church, then I'll start respecting him and submitting to him." What is the problem with that attitude?

How is withholding respect, honor, love, or physical intimacy a type of revenge or payback?

What does the Bible say about revenge in these verses?
Romans 12:17-21

1 Peter 3:9

Proverbs 24:29

1 Thessalonians 5:15

Let's look at the particulars of lovemaking described in Song of Solomon 7. As I mentioned before, it has been said that when it comes to lovemaking, women long for gentleness and men long for responsiveness. How do we see both of these actions and reactions in Song of Solomon Chapter 7?

Romance comes naturally when you're in the dating stage of a relationship. As a marriage matures and becomes packed with activities and responsibilities, romance takes intentionality.

When you became a Christian, how did you grow in your relationship with Christ?

Did it come naturally or did you have to institute some disciplines or practices? If so, what were they?

Since marriage is a reflection of our relationship with Christ, what disciplines do married couples need to establish to help their relationship thrive?

Make a list of 10 ways that you will be intentional to keep romance alive in your marriage.

1.

2.

3.

4.

5.

6.

7.

8.

9.

10.

What impacted your most in *Lovestruck* Chapter 10?

What impacted you most in the *Lovestruck* Bible Study Guide Lesson 10?

Reflect

What disciplines have you established to grow in your relationship with Christ?

What disciplines have you established to grow in your relationship with your husband?

Ponder the idea of something old and something new when it comes to lovemaking. Why do you think God made sure that idea was included in Song of Solomon?

Make a list of 20 new ways you can romance your husband over the next several months. This doesn't have to be all sexual. Writing "I love you" on the bathroom mirror, or leaving a ticket under his windshield for being the most handsome man alive will make his heart soar.

* For great ideas, see Sharon's book, The 14-Day Romance Challenge.

1.

2.

3.

4.

5.

6.

7.

8.

9.

10.

11.

12.

13.

14.

15.

16.

17.

18.

19.

20.

Lesson Eleven

Unquenchable, Unstoppable, Unsurpassable Love

. . . .

We've seen that the theme of Song of Solomon is sexual passion between a husband and a wife for a lifetime. The word "lifetime" is the undercurrent that runs through the Shulammite's final words in Chapter 8. "Many waters cannot quench love, rivers cannot wash it away" (8:7).

All through the Bible, God modeled what a lasting covenant should look like. His "bride," the Israelites and later the Church, sure didn't make it easy. Old Testament children of the Old Covenant—the Jews—and New Testament children of the New Covenant—Christ followers—have been unfaithful time and time again. And yet God keeps giving, forgiving and taking us back.

What do the following verses tell us about God's unstoppable, unquenchable, invaluable love for us?

Isaiah 54:5-8

Ezekiel 16:59-60

Hosea 14:2,4

How do those verses relate to the relationship of an earthly husband and wife?

Let's think about this for a moment:

Why did you marry your husband?

What did the commitment mean to you at the time?

What does that commitment mean to you today?

What is the danger of a marriage based solely on emotions?

What is the beauty of a marriage based on commitment?

Real love implies permanence. When the Shulammite said, "Place me like a seal over your heart" (8:6), that implied permanence. In Bible times, a seal guaranteed security or indicated ownership. I think she meant both in this verse.

However, a seal was only as good as the one doing the sealing.

How are we sealed to our heavenly Bridegroom, Jesus? (Ephesians 1:13-14; 4:30; 2 Corinthians 1:21-22)

Who did the sealing?

"Wedding vows are not a declaration of present love but a mutually binding promise of future love. A wedding should not be primarily a celebration of how loving you feel now—that can safely be assumed. Rather, in a wedding you stand up before God, your family, and all the main institutions of society, and you promise to be loving, faithful, and true to the other person in the future, regardless of undulating internal feelings or external circumstances." [18]

I know the next few questions are going to be painful for some, but we'd be remiss not to see what the Bible says about divorce.

What did the prophet Micah say about God's view of divorce? (Malachi 2:16)

What did Jesus teach about God's original intent for marriage? (Matthew 19:1-9)

Back in Bible times, a wife wasn't allowed to divorce her husband, but a husband could divorce his wife for the smallest offense. If she burnt the toast, he could toss her out. How did Jesus' teaching in Matthew about divorce honor and protect women?

What exceptions did Jesus mention in Matthew 19:1-19 and Paul mention in 1 Corinthians 7:10-16?

If you have already experienced divorce, please know that God has not now nor will He ever abandon you. He loves you and longs to heal your broken places and fill your empty spaces. He is a God of grace and new beginnings! Don't let the devil tell you anything less. What is the truth of Romans 8:1-2?

Early romantic love is rather easy. Someone falls in love with whom he or she thinks the person is—the idea of him or her. How is being deeply known and fully loved which comes with the passing years different from being slightly known and giddily loved when the relationship is in its genesis?

What does Proverbs 19:22a say is a person's greatest desire?

The Hebrew word used for "unfailing love" in Proverbs 19:22 is *chesed*. Bible scholars have had a difficult time translating the word *chesed* into English because there is not a good equivalent. It is often translated "loving kindness," "steadfast love," "mercy" or "loyalty." It is a covenant love that will never change.

We hope for that sort of love from the person we marry. We're promised that sort of love from God (Jeremiah 31:3).

A successful marriage cannot be defined as a husband and wife simply staying together for a lifetime. A couple can be absolutely miserable their entire married life and endure each other to the end. I wouldn't call that successful. How would you define a successful marriage?

One of the key factors to a successful, deep abiding love is intimate friendship. When your husband is your best friend, the cord of love becomes a steel cable.

What do the following verses teach us about friendship and how do they relate to marriage?
Proverbs 17:17

Proverbs 18:24

Proverbs 27:9

Proverbs 27:17

Tim Keller said,

> "While erotic love can be depicted as two people looking at one another, friendship can be depicted as two people standing side by side looking at the same object and being stirred and entranced by it together." [19]

Explain what you think Keller means by that statement.

C.S. Lewis says friendships are formed when there is a "common thread" that runs through shared experiences and interests with another.

How do common interests build friendship and anchor marriage?

What is the most important thread that a husband and wife can share? (1 Corinthians 6:17)

Read and record Proverbs 2:16-17.

The NIV translates the verse "partner of her youth." The ESV and NASB translations say, "companion of her youth." The Greek word translated "partner" or "companion" is *allup*, and means "special confidant" or "best friend."

How is your husband your best friend and confidant?

If he isn't your best friend, can you think of any ways to deepen your friendship?

Ways to spend quality time together?

Ways to share your deepest hurts and hopes?

Ways to work toward a common goal or goals?

I know that question might be difficult for some. If you don't have shared interests other than your children, then that is reason for pause. Developing lifelong friendship swings on the hinges of shared interests.

According to the following verses, what are qualities of an intimate, transparent, and consistent friendship? How do each of these relate to marriage? How can you live out each of these with your husband? Romans 12:9-10

Hebrews 3:13

Hebrews 10:24

Galatians 6:2

1 Thessalonians 5:11,14-15

How do shared experiences deepen the river of love?

I know we've looked at this verse before, but read and record the first sentence of 1 Corinthians 13:8a. Go to Biblehub.com or Biblegateway.com and record this verse from these various translations. New Living Translation

English Standard Version

Contemporary English Version

Good New Translation

The Message (a paraphrase)

Wine is often said to grow better with age. My research revealed that isn't true for all wines, but for some.

All through this love song, both Solomon and the Shulammite compare their love and lovemaking to wine. Note the comparisons in the following verses:
Song of Solomon 1:2

Song of Solomon 1:4b

Song of Solomon 4:10

Song of Solomon 5:1

Song of Solomon 7:2

Song of Solomon 7:9

Song of Solomon 8:2

What does Luke 5:39 tell us about the beauty of aged wine? (Being a bit of aged wine myself, I really like this verse.)

I don't know much about aging wine, but I do know it is somewhat of an art form with several variables to bring about the best result. In my research I stumbled across the following:

> "Tannins are a natural preservative, capable of keeping a bottle of wine palatable for 40 years or longer. When a wine is young, its tannins give it a bitter and astringent flavor. In time, the tannins dissipate and cause the body of the wine to develop its own "bouquet," or aroma and essence. The bouquet improves over time, imparting a smooth, rich flavor without the bitterness of a younger wine." [20]

After being married for over 35 years, I can promise you this...love and lovemaking can grow better with time. Yes, there are several variables to bring about the best result. Honor, respect, shared interests, open communication, spiritual oneness...all of what we have seen with the maturing of love throughout the pages of Song of Solomon.

While we're talking about wine, let's look at Jesus' first miracle, when He turned the water into wine at the wedding in Cana of Galilee. Read John 2:1-11 and answer the following questions.

Where was Jesus?

Who was with Him?

What does this tell you about Jesus that He would attend such a celebration?

A wedding ceremony could last up to seven days. It was terribly embarrassing for the hosting family to run out of wine.

Read and record what Mary told the servants to do in verse 5.

I love reading the Bible in different translations. The NASB translates verse 5 this way: "Whatever he says to you, do it." This is a key verse for discovering peace and purpose in our lives.

Did Jesus need the servant's help for this miracle? (Before you answer this question, how did God provide the manna for the children of Israel as they wandered in the desert in Exodus 16:4?)

Why do you think He involved the servants?

Jesus could just as easily have made the wine miraculously appear without anyone's help. But Jesus chose to allow His servants to join Him in His work, just as He still chooses to invite us to join Him today. He allows us to participate in His ministry and gives us the opportunity to be blessed when we obey.

How much water did Jesus tell the servants to put in the six water pots?

How much did He turn into wine?

Supposed they had only filled the water pots half-way. How much would Jesus have turned into wine?

If you want Jesus to transform your marriage and your sexual intimacy (water to wine), then how much are you willing to give Him? He will transform just as much as you are willing to put in the pot.

Jesus is in the transformation business: sadness into gladness, sinners into saints, and miseries into ministries. The most important transformation that occurs in us is when we accept Jesus Christ and become one spiritually with Him (2 Corinthians 5:17).

The second most important transformation that occurs in a person's life is when that individual marries and becomes "one flesh" with another person. If you haven't been transformed by your marriage, you and your spouse probably haven't been married very long. Marriage changes us. When we let Jesus work miracles in our marriage, He will take something good and make it better. But just as He desired the servants' participation, He desires ours. He wants us to fill our marriage conduits "to the brim," so that He can transform it all. And as Mary said, "Whatever he says to you, do it," even it if doesn't make sense to you.

Then, when the years pass and you grow old with the husband of your youth, you can say with the headwaiter at the wedding in Cana, "You've saved the best to now."

What impacted you most in *Lovestruck* Chapter 11?

What impacted you most in the *Lovestruck* Bible Study Guide Lesson 11?

Reflect

What marriages have you observed that have lasted a lifetime?

Where do you hope to see your marriage 5, 10, or 20 years from now?

What changes do you need to put into practice to make that a reality?

Physical intimacy that makes God stand up and cheer doesn't simply happen throughout the lifetime of a marriage. It takes intentionality. From this study, how are you going to be intentional about maintaining and deepening physical intimacy in your marriage?

What would you say if someone asked you, "What is Song of Solomon about?"

I am so proud of you for finishing this study. I pray that God will continue to bless you and your marriage and that you will say, "God has saved the best till last."

[1] http://www1.cbn.com/family/god-formed-the-man-and-fashioned-the-woman

[2] Dr. Gary Smalley and Ted Cunningham, The Language of Sex (Ventura, CA: Regal: 2008) 55.

[3] Stephen and Judith Schwamback, For Lovers Only (Eugene, OR: Harvest House Publishers, 1990) 127.

[4] Tim Keller, The Meaning of Marriage (New York, NY: Penguin Books, 2011) 256.

[5] Merrill R. Unger, Unger's Bible Dictionary, (Chicago, IL: Moody Press, 1966) 207-208

[6] Tim Keller, The Meaning of Marriage, 270-271.

[7] http://biblehub.com/greek/2540.htm

[8] Tommy Thomas, Song of Solomon: God's best for love, marriage, sex and romance study guide
(Plano, TX: Hudson Productions, 2007) 47.

[9] Dr. Gary Smalley and Ted Cunningham, The Language of Sex (Ventura, CA: Regal, 2008), 27.

[10] https://www.gotquestions.org/Bible-anger.html

[11] http://traciemiles.com/7-ways-to-know-when-anger-is-sin/

[12] Gary & Greg Smalley, The Covenant Marriage, (Minneapolis, MN: Bethany House, 2014), 2015.

[13] Tim Keller, The Meaning of Marriage, 41.

[14] Tim Keller, The Meaning of Marriage, 43-44.

[15] http://biblehub.com/greek/1247.htm

[16] Tim Keller, The Meaning of Marriage, 57

[17] https://www.desiringgod.org/articles/six-things-submission-is-not

[18] Tim Keller, The Meaning of Marriage, 91.

[19] Tim Keller, The Meaning of Marriage, 123-124.

[20] http://www.cellaraiders.com/-a-25.html

About the Author

Sharon Jaynes has been encouraging and equipping women through ministry for more than twenty-five years. She served as vice president and radio cohost of Proverbs 31 Ministries for ten years and currently writes for their on-line devotions. Sharon is co-founder of Girlfriends in God, Inc., and is also a conference speaker, Bible teacher, and author of more then twenty books. She has been romancing her husband, Steve for thirty-eight years, and they make their home in Weddington, NC.

Other Marriage Resources by Sharon Jaynes

 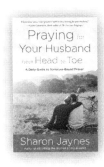 

The Praying Wives App

the PRAYING WIVES club

Made in the USA
Columbia, SC
10 September 2019